What's Silly?

by Niki Yektai

illustrated by Susannah Ryan

A TRUMPET CLUB SPECIAL EDITION

Published by The Trumpet Club
1540 Broadway, New York, New York 10036

Text copyright © 1989 by Helene Niki Yektai
Illustrations copyright © 1989 by Susannah Ryan

ISBN: 0-440-84418-5

This edition published by arrangement with
Clarion Books/Houghton Mifflin Company
Printed in the United States of America
February 1991

10 9 8 7 6 5 4 3 2
UPC

Something is silly.

The SKIRT!

What's silly now?

The SHAVING CREAM!

Now what's silly?

The HAT and DOG!

Something is silly.

The TREES!

What is silly?

The NEST and HAT!

What's silly here?

The KETCHUP and COMB!

Now what's silly?

The CAR and BOAT!

Something is very silly.

The BATHROOM and TV!

Now what's silly?

The FLOWERS and SPAGHETTI!

What's silly here?

The DISHES and SHOES!

What is silly?

The DOG and BABY!

What's silly outside?

The STARS and MOON!

What's silly inside?

The SHEETS and BLANKETS!

That's better. Good night!

Not quite!